SCHOTT PIANO LOUNGE

Swing Standards

18 Famous Songs
18 bekannte Melodien

arranged by / arrangiert von
Carsten Gerlitz

ED 20115
ISMN 979-0-001-14639-5

www.schott-music.com

Mainz · London · Berlin · Madrid · New York · Paris · Prague · Tokyo · Toronto

Die CD wurde produziert im greenlandmusicstudio, Berlin
Klavier und Programmierung: Carsten Gerlitz
Schlagzeug: Stephan Genze

Bestellnummer: ED 20115
ISMN 979-0-001-14639-5
© 2007 Schott Music GmbH & Co. KG, Mainz
Printed in Germany · BSS 52354

Inhalt / Contents

Moonlight Serenade

Musik: Glenn Miller
Text: Mitchell Parish
Arrangement: Carsten Gerlitz

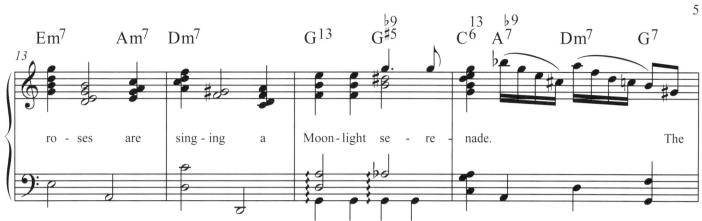

ro - ses are sing - ing a Moon - light se - re - nade. The

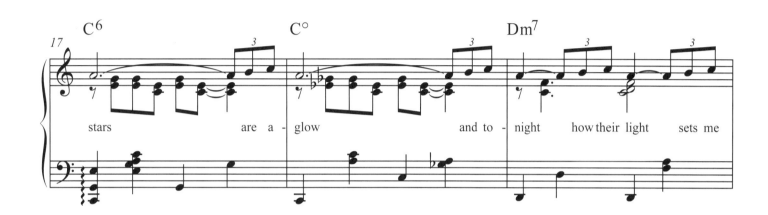

stars are a - glow and to - night how their light sets me

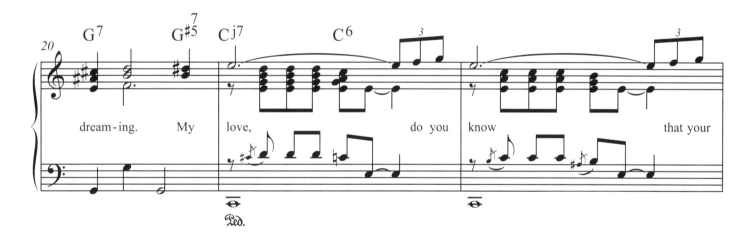

dream - ing. My love, do you know that your

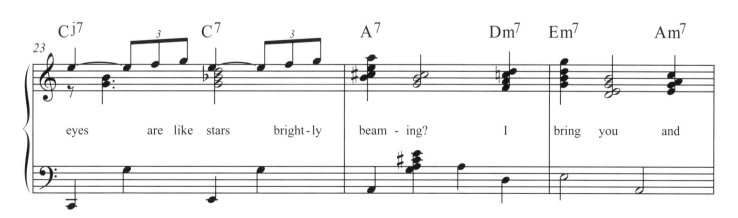

eyes are like stars bright - ly beam - ing? I bring you and

sing you a Moon - light se - re - nade.

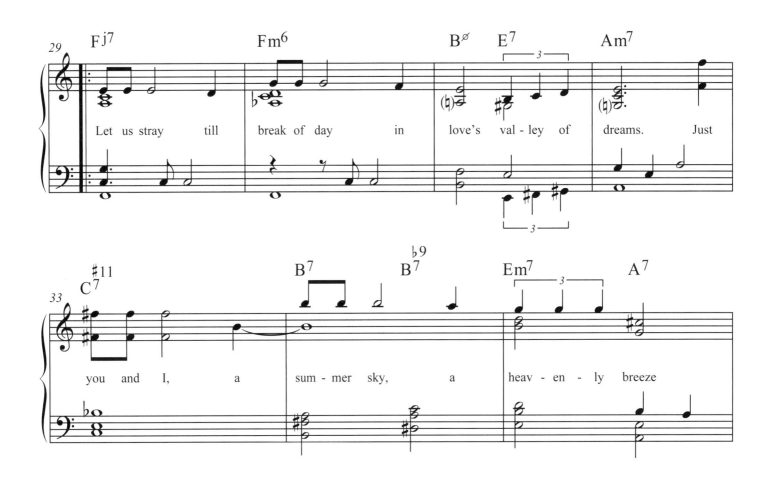

Let us stray till break of day in love's val - ley of dreams. Just

you and I, a sum - mer sky, a heav - en - ly breeze

kiss - ing the trees. So don't let me wait, come to

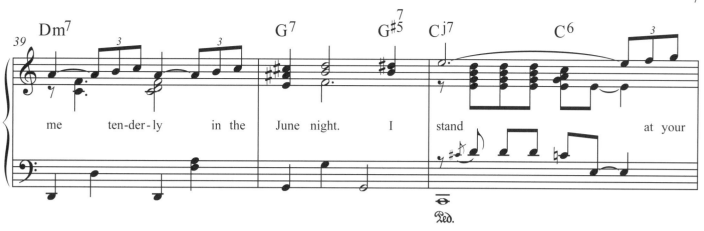

me ten-der-ly in the June night. I stand at your

gate and I sing you a song in the moon-light, a

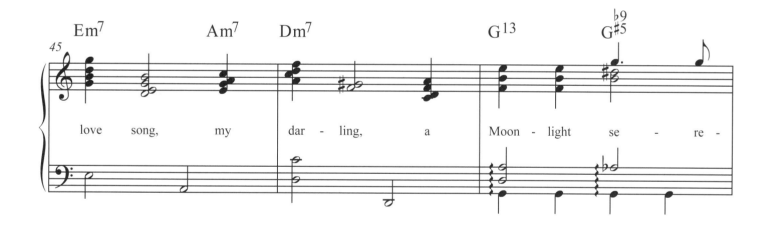

love song, my dar-ling, a Moon - light se - re -

nade. *even* ♪ nade. *rit.*

Just a Gigolo

Musik: Leonello Casucci
Text: Julius Brammer, Irving Caesar
Arrangement: Carsten Gerlitz

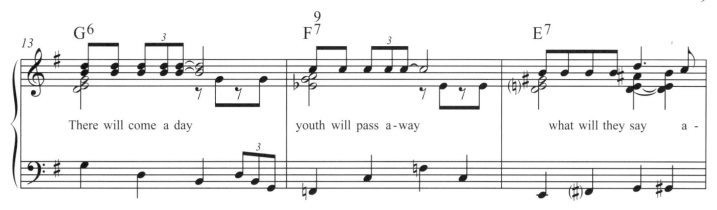

There will come a day   youth will pass a-way   what will they say a-

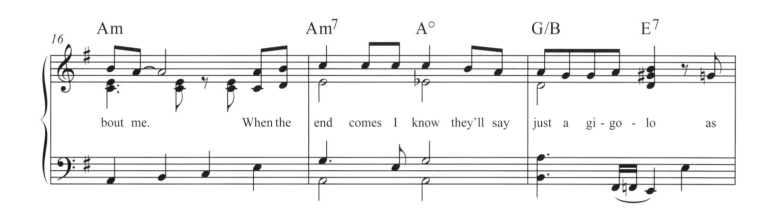

bout me.   When the end comes I know they'll say   just a gi-go-lo   as

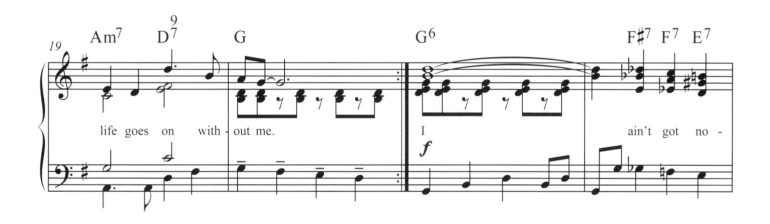

life goes on with-out me.   I   ain't got no-

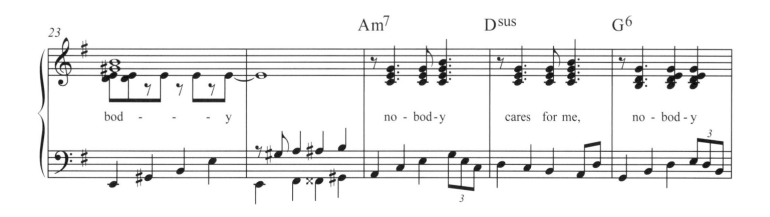

bod - - y   no-bod-y   cares for me,   no-bod-y

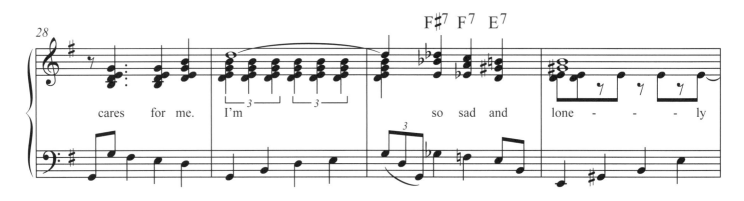

cares for me. I'm so sad and lone - - ly

sad and lone-ly 'cause I ain't so bad.

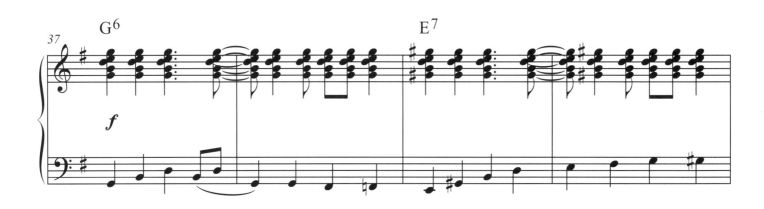

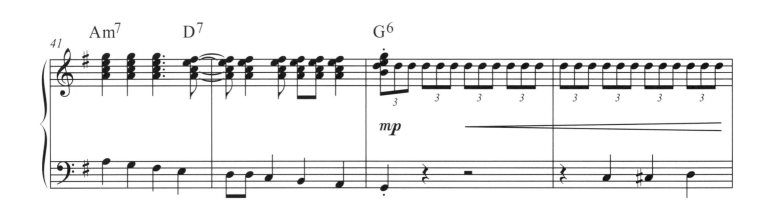

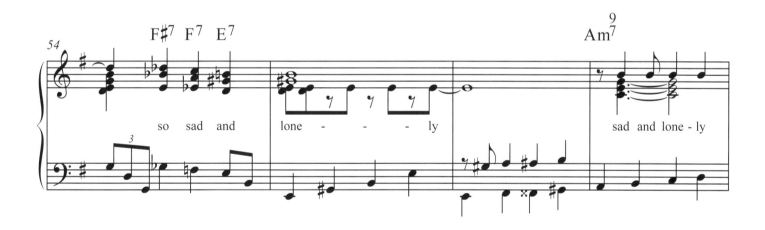

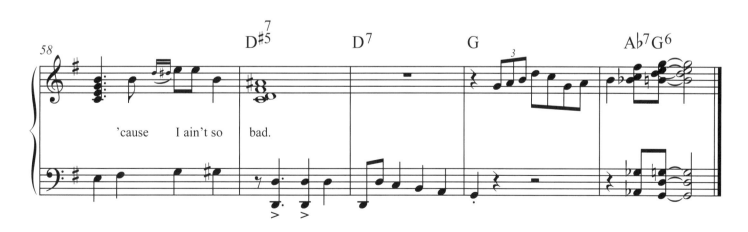

Take the A Train

Musik und Text: Billy Strayhorn
Arrangement: Carsten Gerlitz

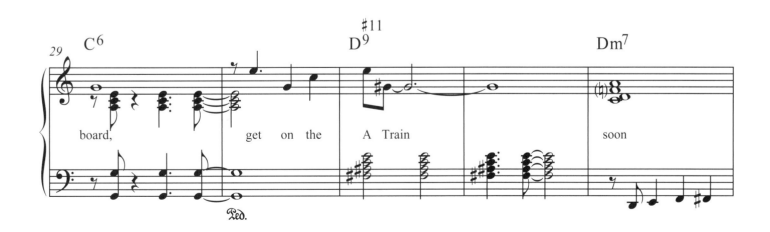

you will be on Sug - ar Hill in Har - lem.

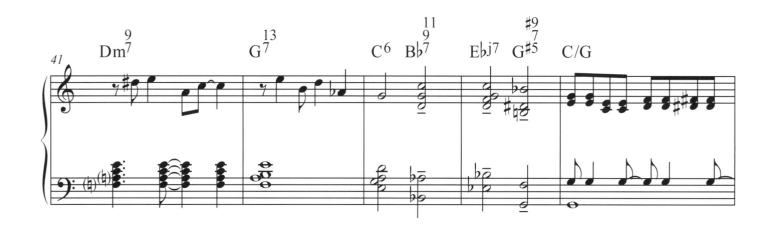

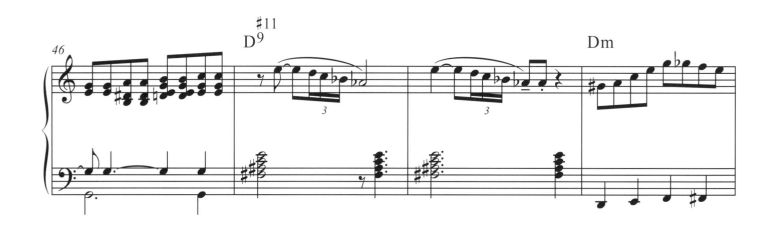

Hur-ry, get on board it's

com-ing listen to those rails a-

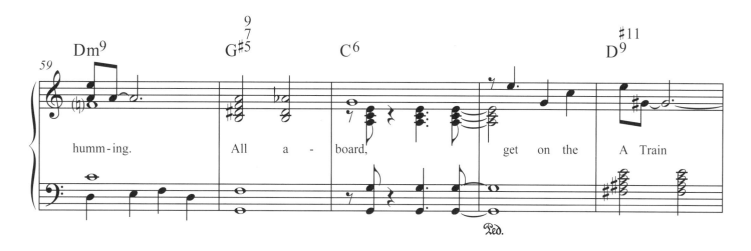

humm-ing. All a-board, get on the A Train

soon you will be on Sug-ar Hill in Har-lem.

There Will Never be Another You

Musik: Harry Warren
Text: Mack Gordon
Arrangement: Carsten Gerlitz

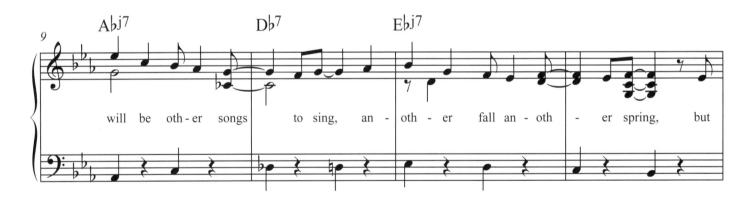

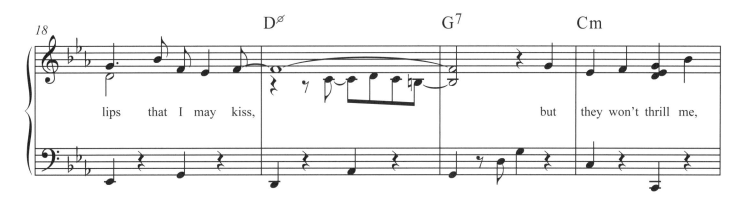

lips that I may kiss, but they won't thrill me,

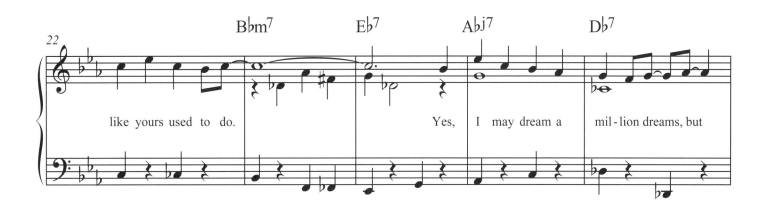

like yours used to do. Yes, I may dream a mil-lion dreams, but

how can they come true, if there will nev-er, ev-er be an-oth-er you.

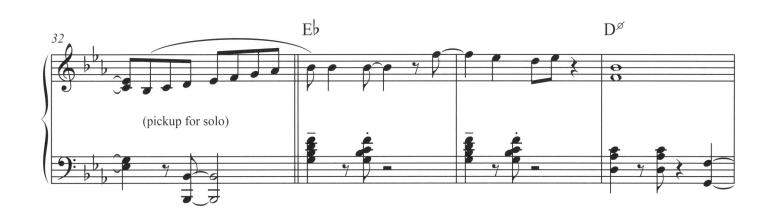

(pickup for solo)

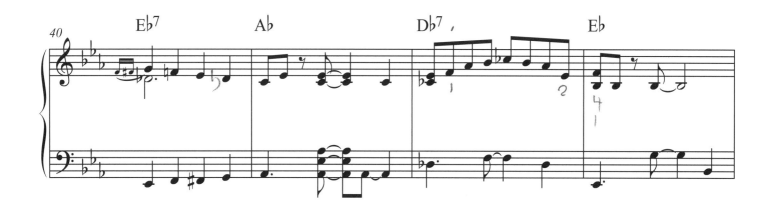

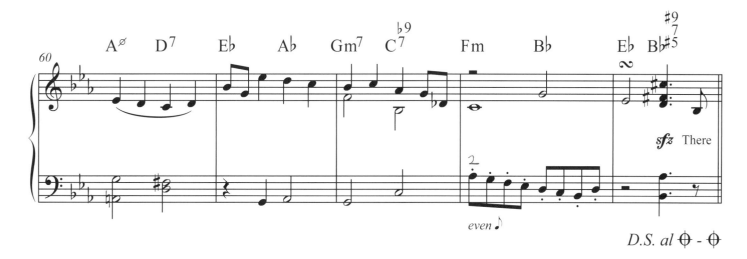

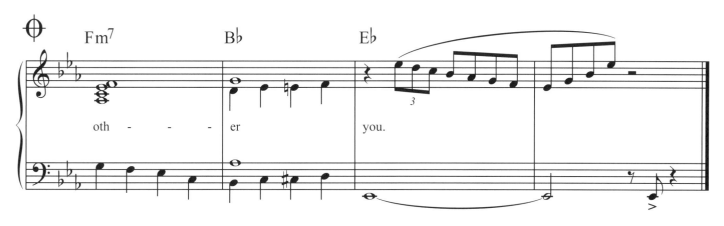

Fly me to the Moon

Musik und Text: Bart Howard
Arrangement: Carsten Gerlitz

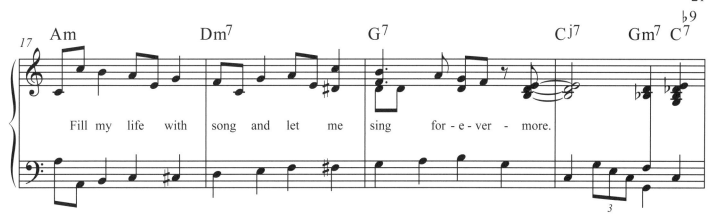

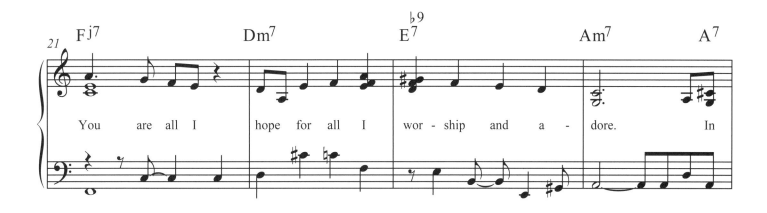

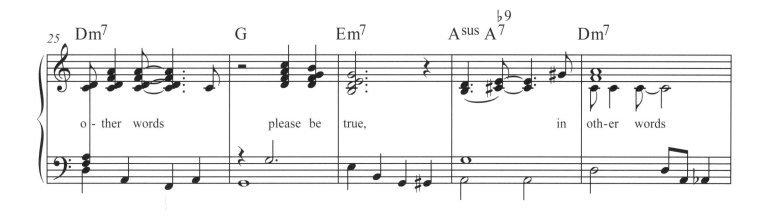

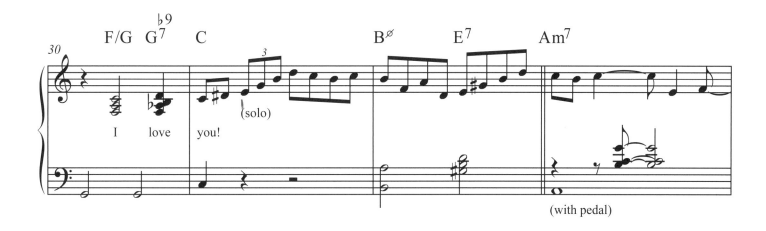

22

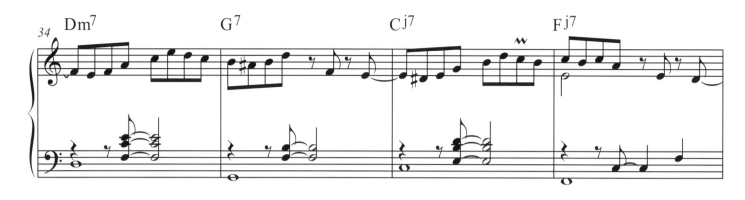

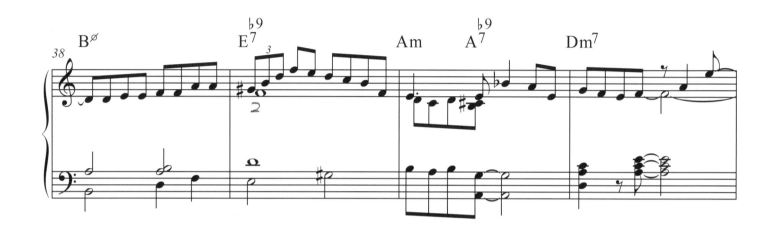

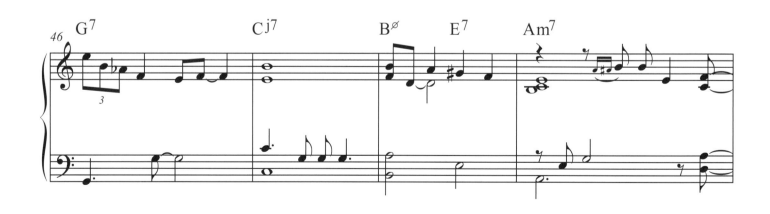

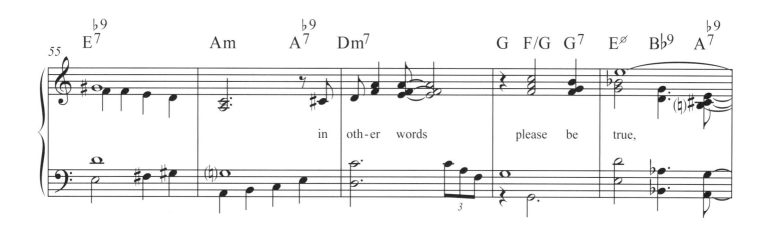

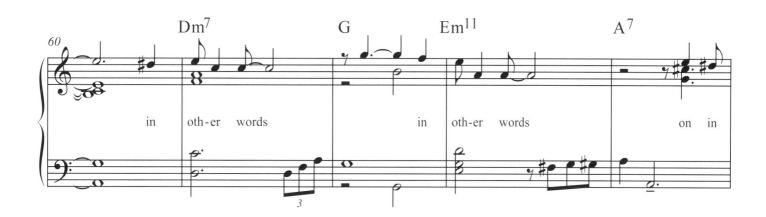

Lullaby of Birdland

Musik: George Shearing
Text: B. Forster
Arrangement: Carsten Gerlitz

bill and coo   when they love?   That's the kind of ma - gic

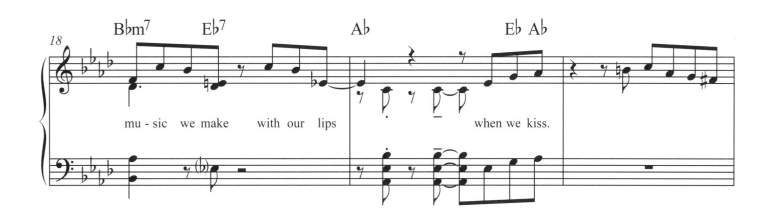

mu - sic we make   with our lips   when we kiss.

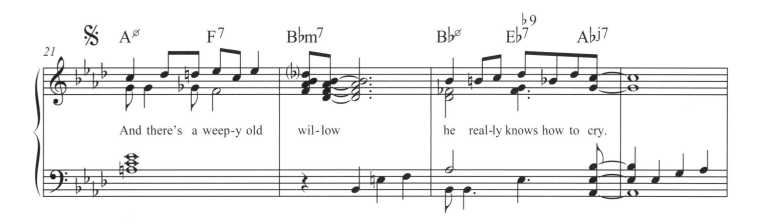

And there's a weep-y old   wil-low   he real-ly knows how to cry.

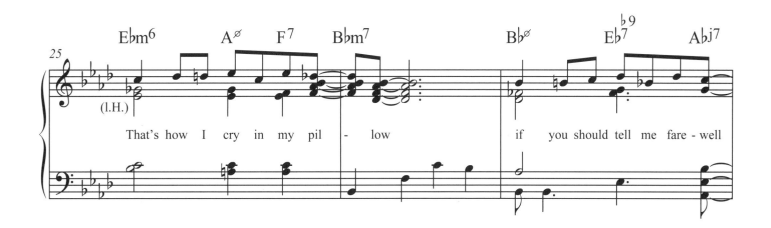

That's how I cry in my pil - low   if you should tell me fare - well

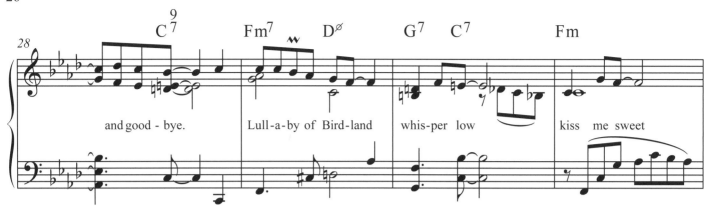

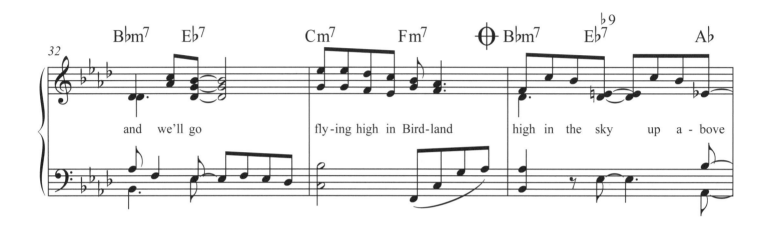

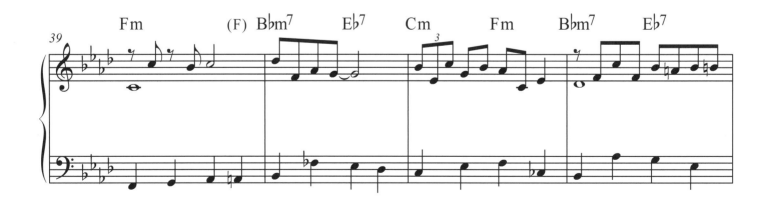

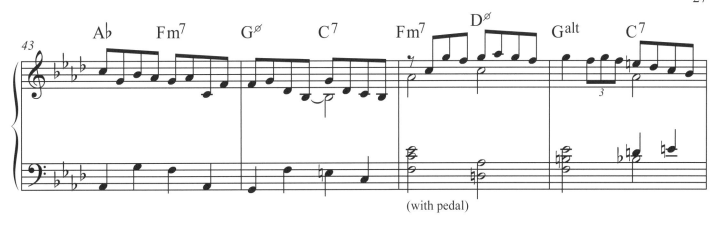

(with pedal)

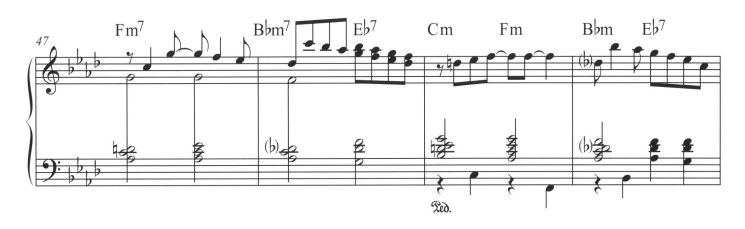

D.S. al
⊕ - ⊕

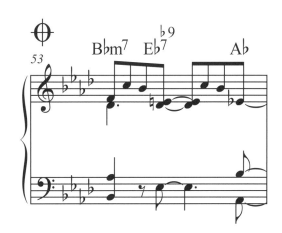

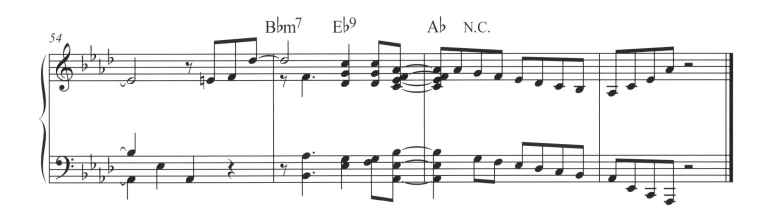

Sentimental Journey

Musik und Text: Les Brown,
Bud Green, Benjamin Homer
Arrangement: Carsten Gerlitz

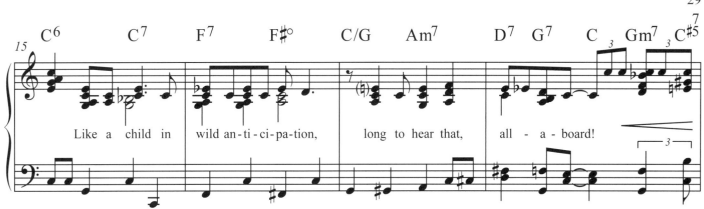

Like a child in wild an-ti-ci-pa-tion, long to hear that, all - a - board!

Sev-en, that's the time we leave at sev-en. I'll be wait-ing up at

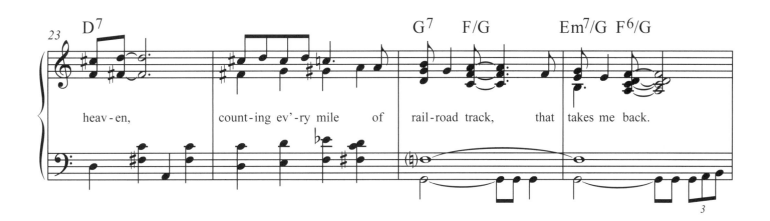

heav-en, count-ing ev'-ry mile of rail-road track, that takes me back.

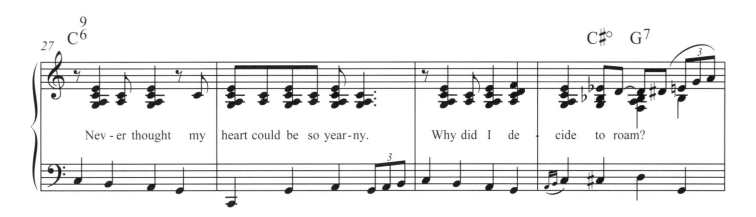

Nev-er thought my heart could be so year-ny. Why did I de - cide to roam?

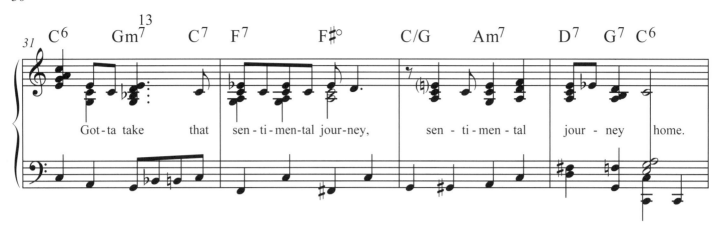

Got-ta take that sen - ti - men-tal jour-ney, sen - ti - men - tal jour - ney home.

(solo)

sempre stacc.
(no pedal)

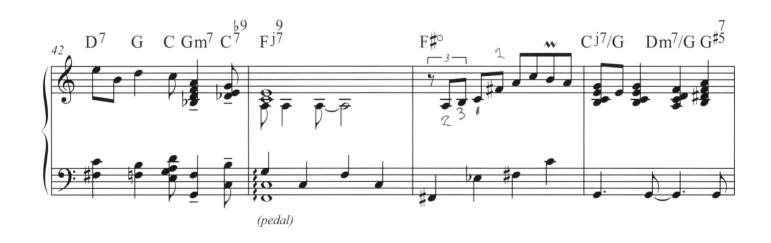

(pedal)

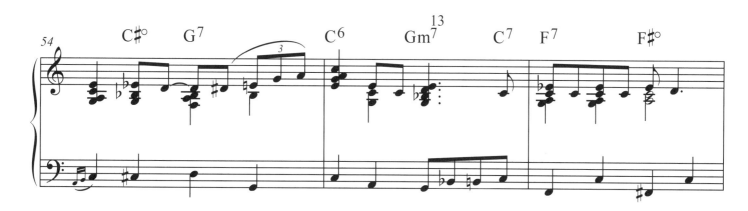

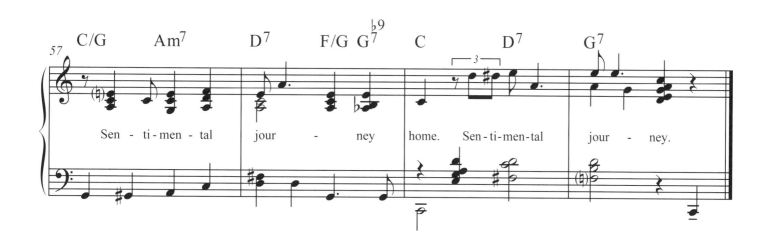

Sen - ti - men - tal   jour - ney   home. Sen - ti - men - tal   jour - ney.

It's only a Papermoon

Musik: Harold Arlen
Text: E. Harburg, Billy Rose
Arrangement: Carsten Gerlitz

your love   it's a hon-ky - tonk pa-rade,   with-out

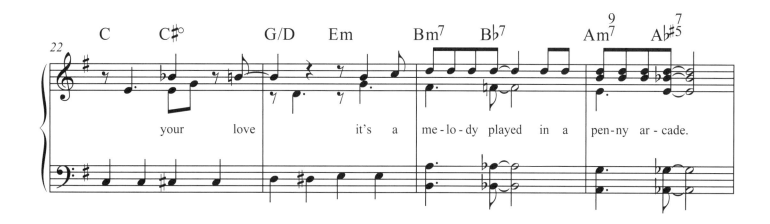

your love   it's a me-lo-dy played in a pen-ny ar-cade.

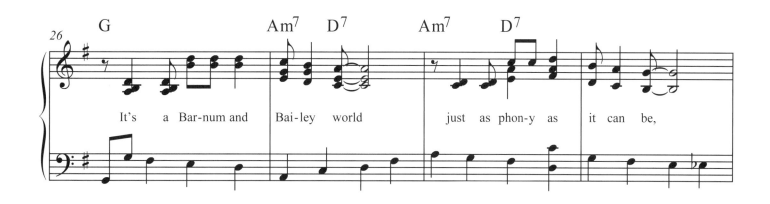

It's a Bar-num and Bai-ley world   just as phon-y as   it can be,

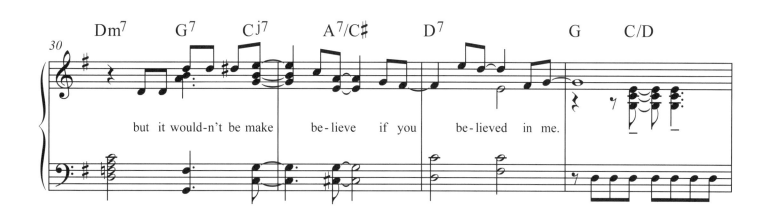

but it would-n't be make be-lieve if you   be-lieved in me.

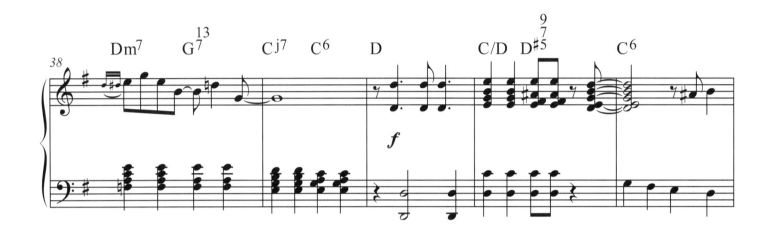

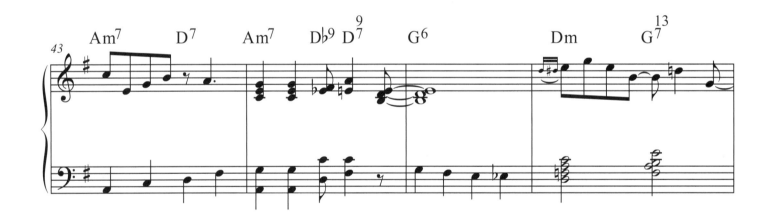

With-out   your   love

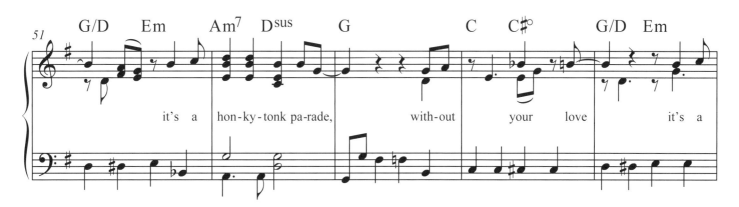

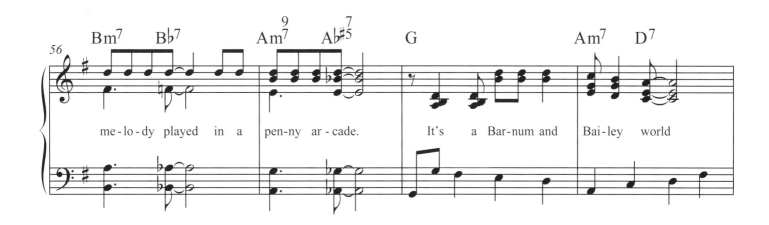

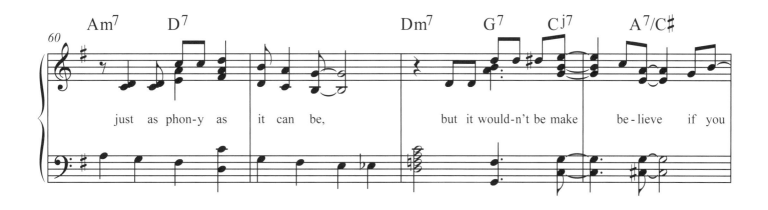

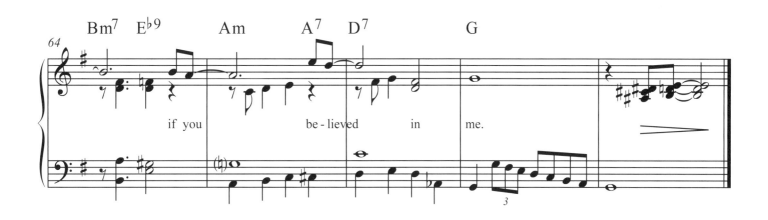

Mack the Knife

(Mackie Messer)

Musik: Kurt Weill
Text: Bertolt Brecht
Arrangement: Carsten Gerlitz

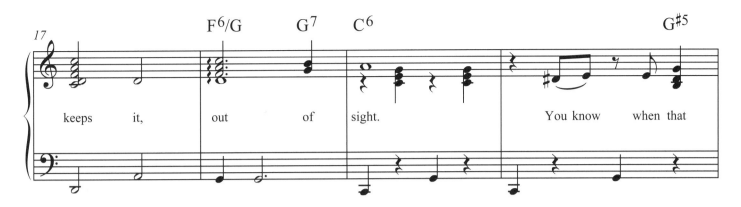

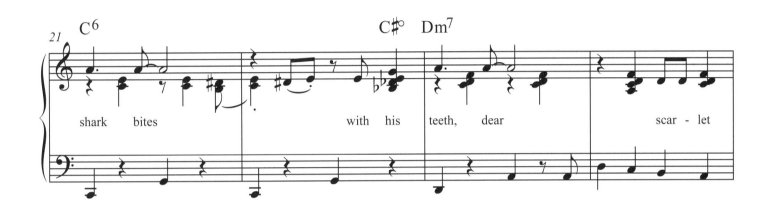

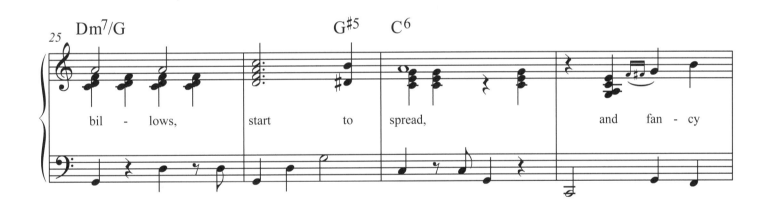

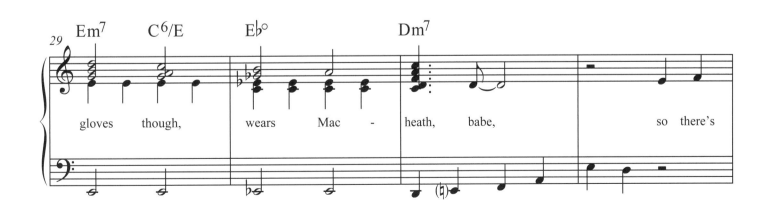

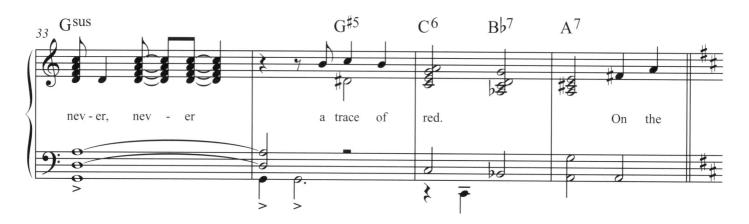

never, never a trace of red. On the

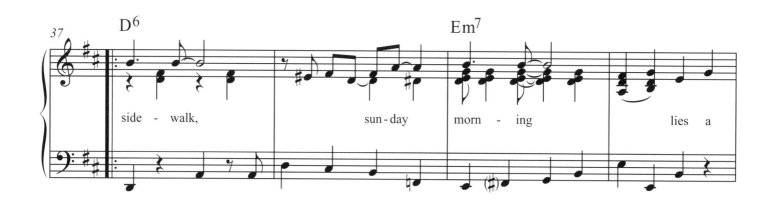

side - walk, sun - day morn - ing lies a

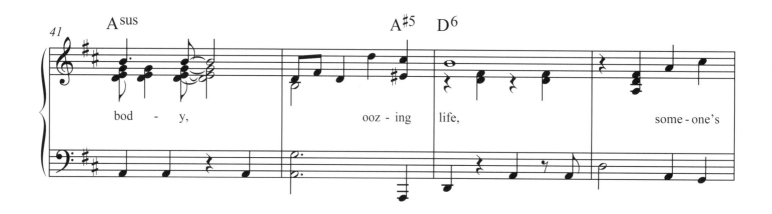

bod - y, ooz - ing life, some - one's

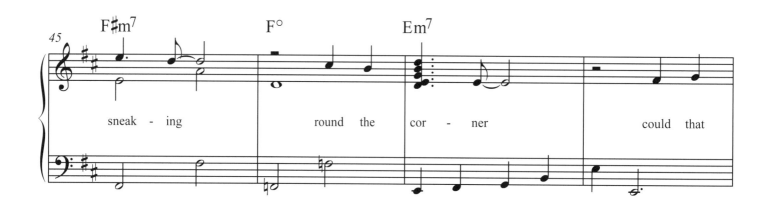

sneak - ing round the cor - ner could that

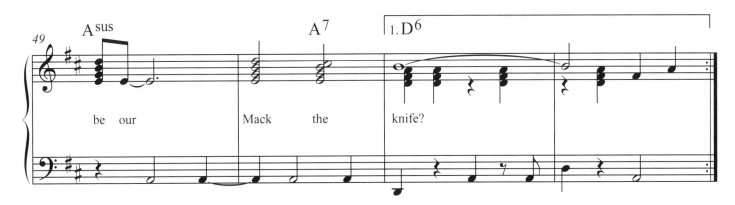

be our   Mack   the   knife?

knife.

even ♪

Mack   the   knife.

4. From a tug boat down by the river
   there's a cement bag just drooping on down,
   that cement's there, it's there for the weight, dear,
   five'll get you ten old Macheath's back in town

Cherokee
(Indian Love Song)

Musik und Text: Ray Noble
Arrangement: Carsten Gerlitz

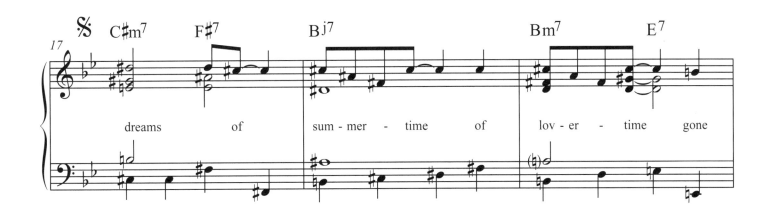

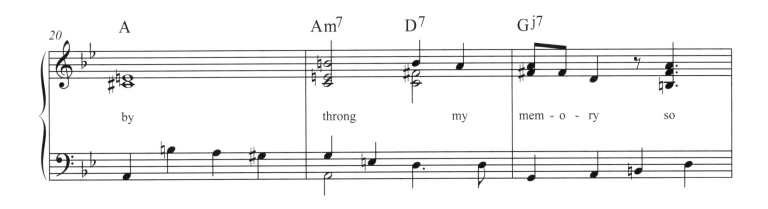

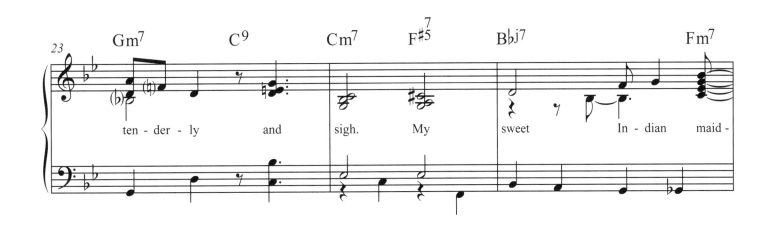

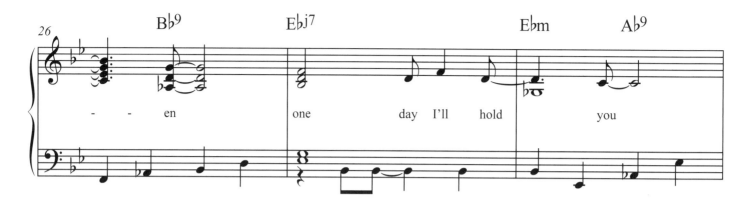

- - en one day I'll hold you

in my arm fold you Cher - o - kee. (pickup)

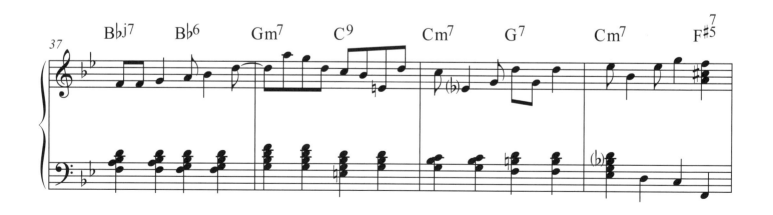

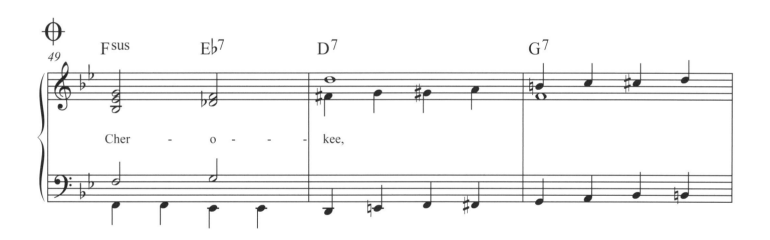

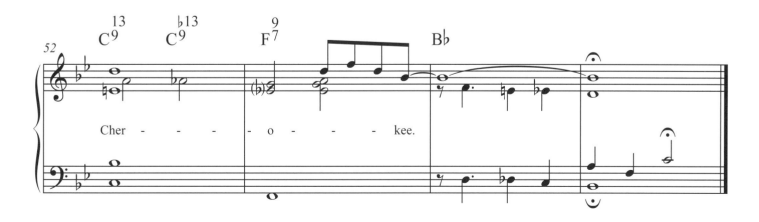

Have You Met Miss Jones?

Musik: Richard Rodgers
Text: Lorenz Hart
Arrangement: Carsten Gerlitz

44

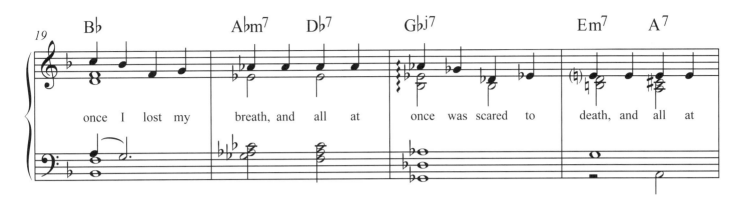

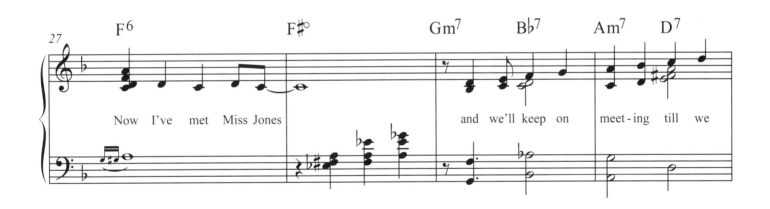

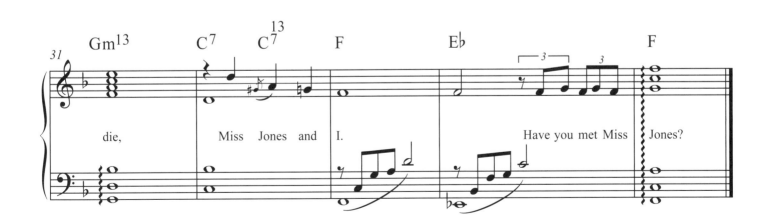

Clair

Musik und Text: Gilbert O'Sullivan
Arrangement: Carsten Gerlitz

Clair, the mo-ment I met you I swear I

felt as if some-thing some - where had happen-ed to me which

I could-n't see then the mo-ment I met you a - gain I

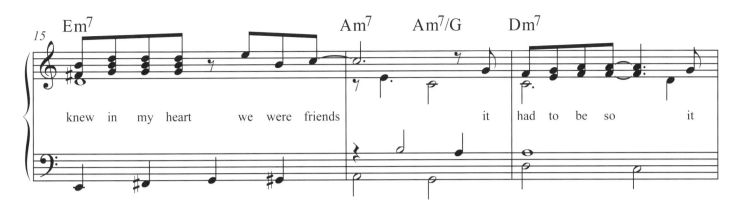

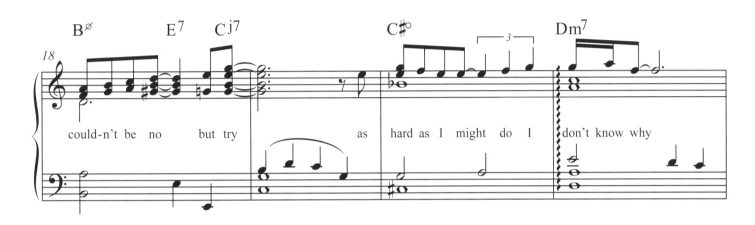

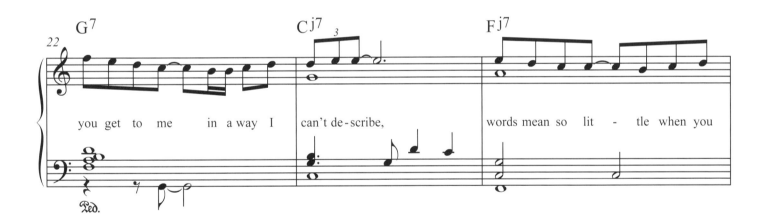

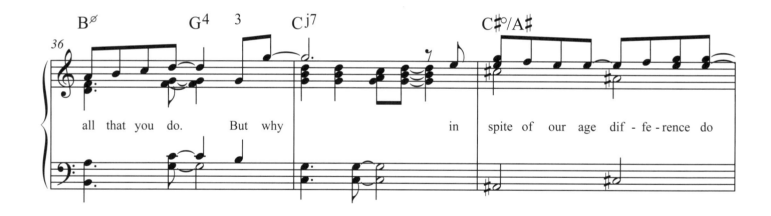

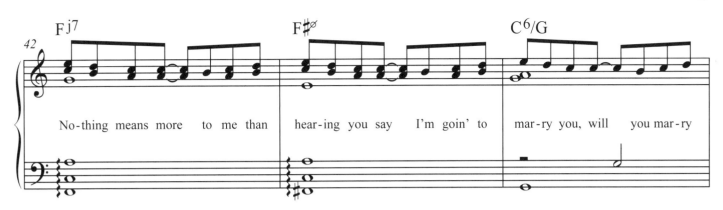

No-thing means more   to me than   hear-ing you say   I'm goin' to   mar-ry you, will   you mar-ry

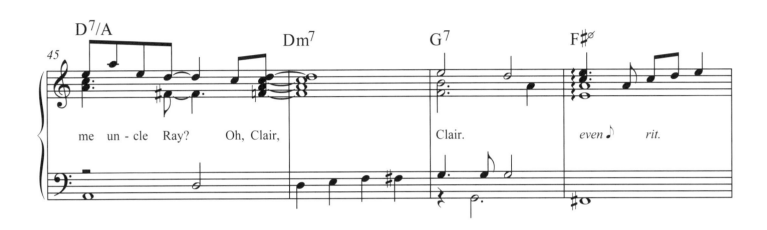

me un-cle Ray?   Oh, Clair,   Clair.   *even* ♪   *rit.*

3. Clair, I've told you before
   Don't you dare
   Get back into bed
   Can't you see that it's late
   No you can't have a drink
   Oh! all right then but wait just a bit
   While I, in an effort to baby sit,
   Catch of my breath what there is left of it.
   You can be murder at this hour of the day
   But in the morning this hour
   Will seem a lifetime away
   Oh! Clair, Clair.

Satin Doll

Music: Duke Ellington, Billy Strayhorn
Words: John Mercer
Arrangement: Carsten Gerlitz

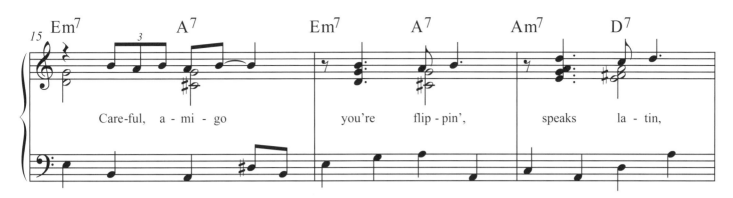

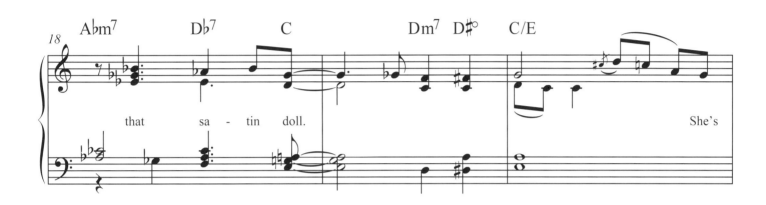

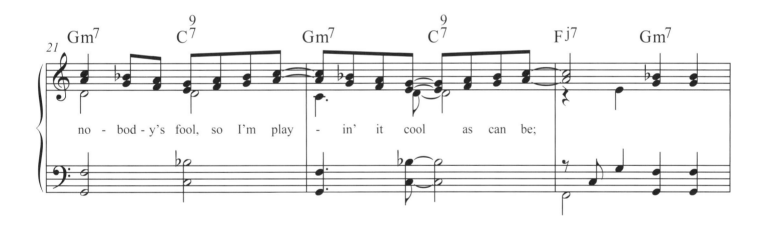

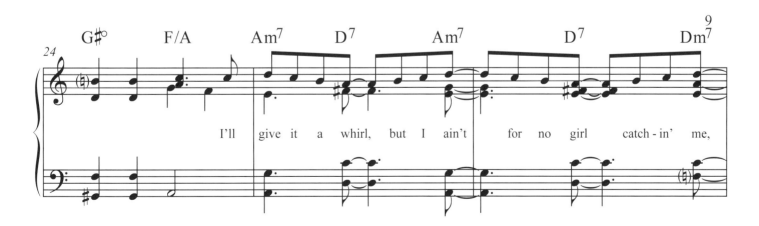

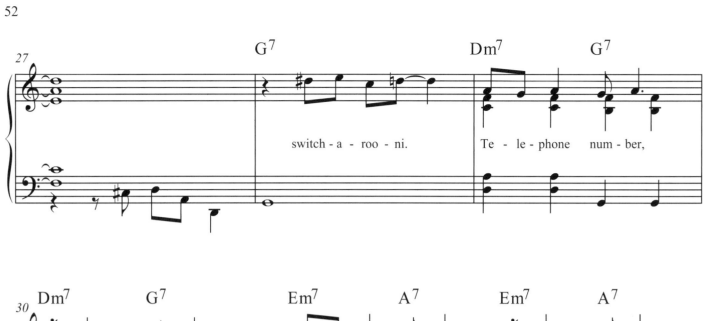

switch - a - roo - ni. Te - le - phone num - ber,

well you know, do - ing my rum - ba with u - no,

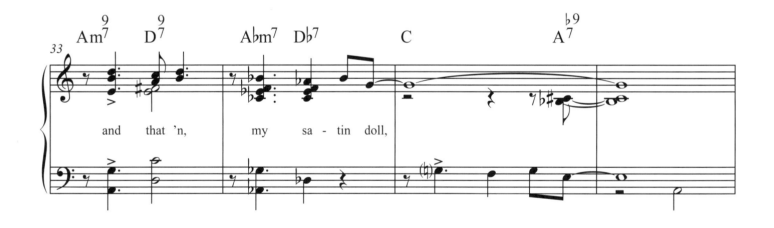

and that 'n, my sa - tin doll,

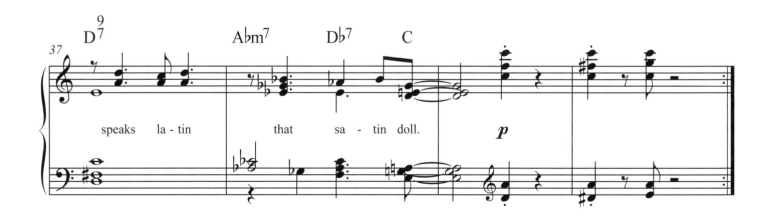

speaks la - tin that sa - tin doll. *p*

Ain't She Sweet

Musik und Text: Ager & Jack Yellin
Arrangement: Carsten Gerlitz

ask you ver - y con - fi - den - tial - ly, ain't she

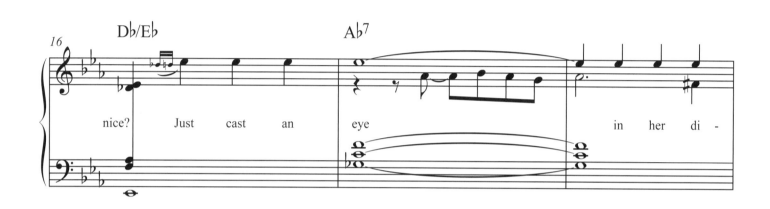

nice? Just cast an eye in her di -

rec - tion, oh me and my,

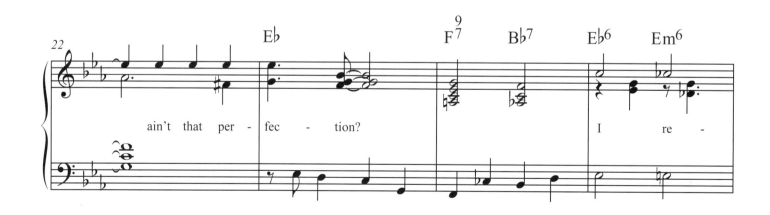

ain't that per - fec - tion? I re -

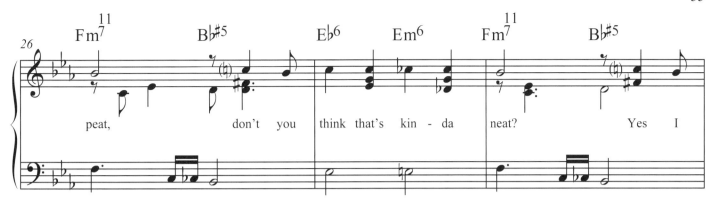

peat, don't you think that's kin - da neat? Yes I

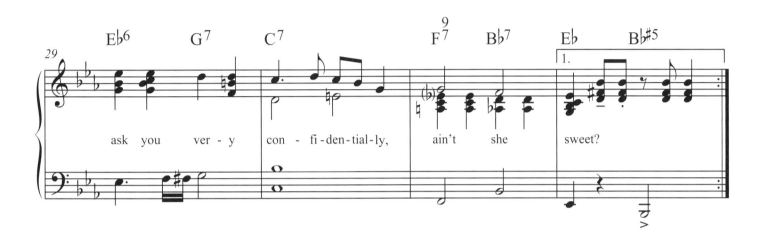

ask you ver - y con - fi -den-tial-ly, ain't she sweet?

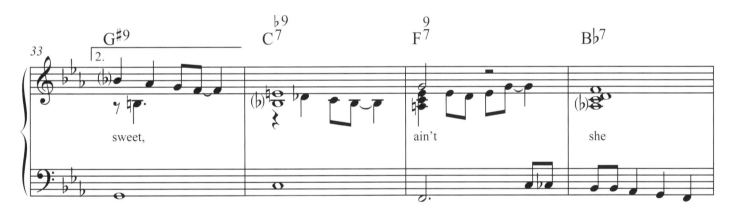

sweet, ain't she

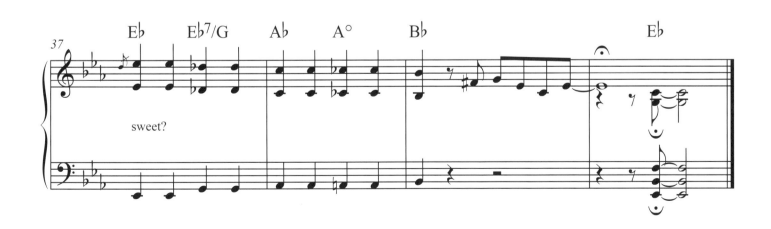

sweet?

Chattanooga Choo Choo

Musik und Text:
Mack Gordon, Harry Warren
Arrangement: Carsten Gerlitz

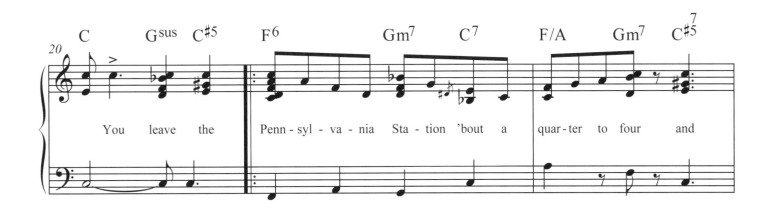

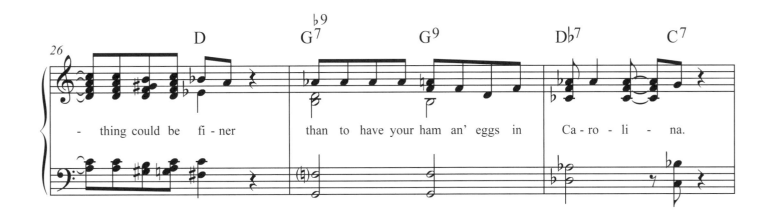

When you hear the whis-tle blow-in' eight to the bar then you know that Ten-nes-see is

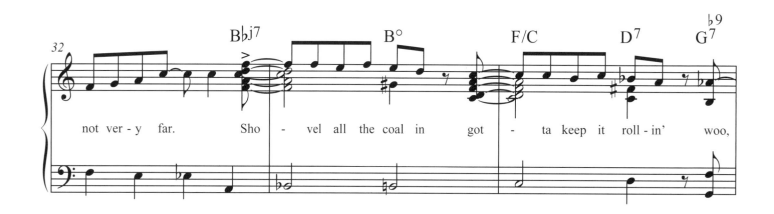

not ver-y far. Sho - vel all the coal in got - ta keep it roll-in' woo,

woo, Chat - ta-noo-ga there you are. There's gon-na be

a cer-tain par-ty at the sta-tion, sa-tin and lace

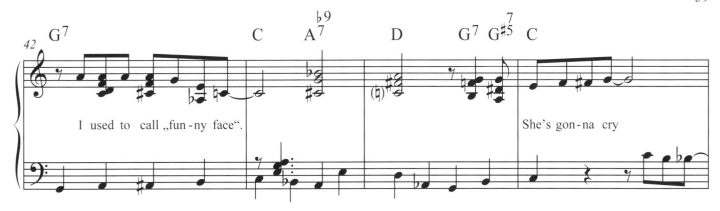

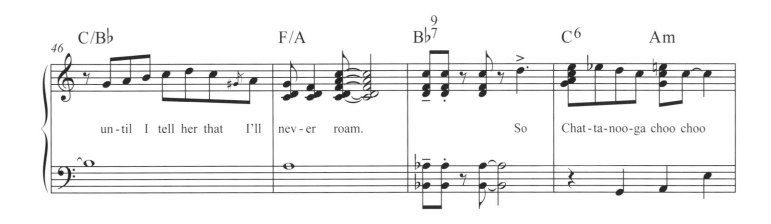

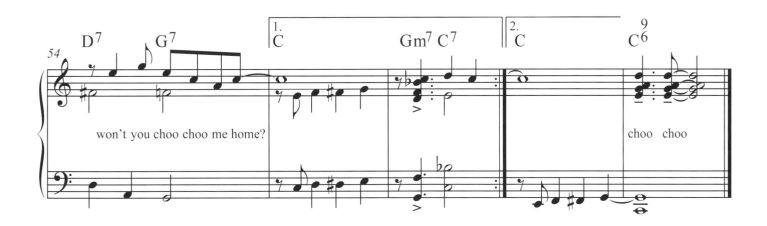

I Get a Kick out of You

Musik und Text: Cole Porter
Arrangement: Carsten Gerlitz

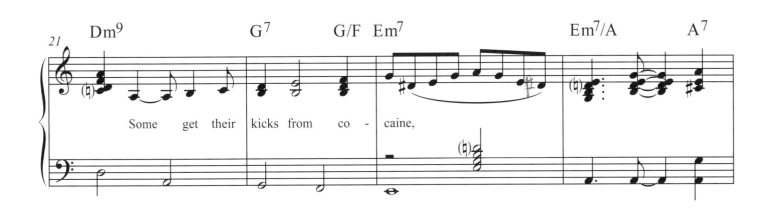

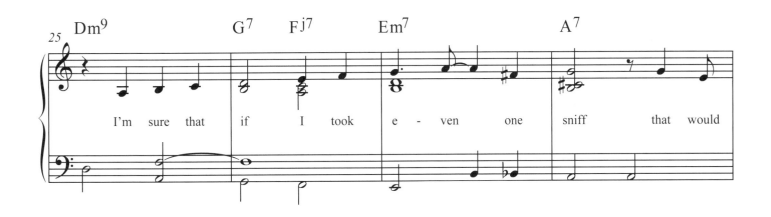

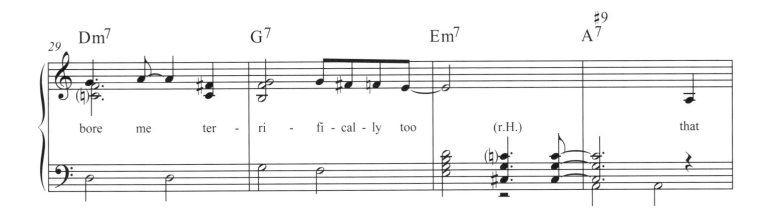

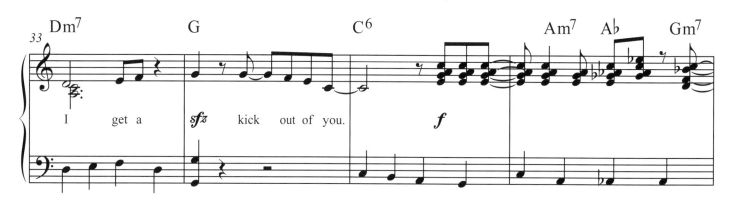

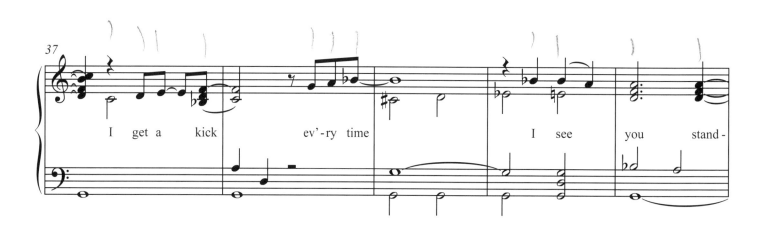

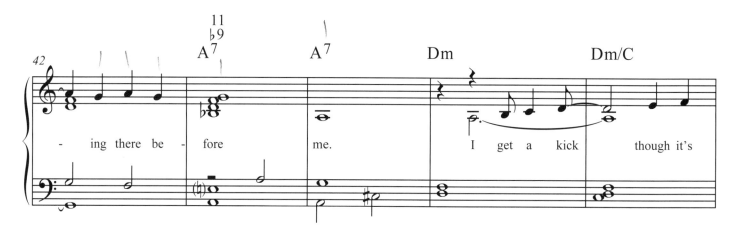

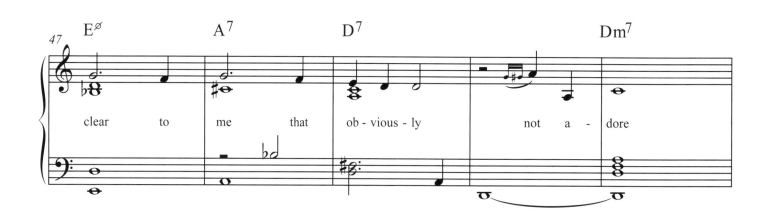

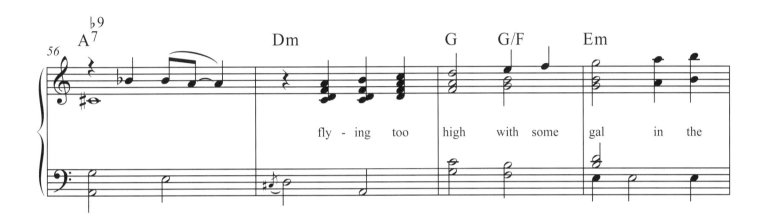

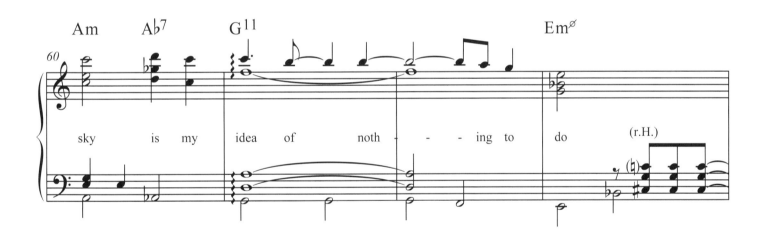

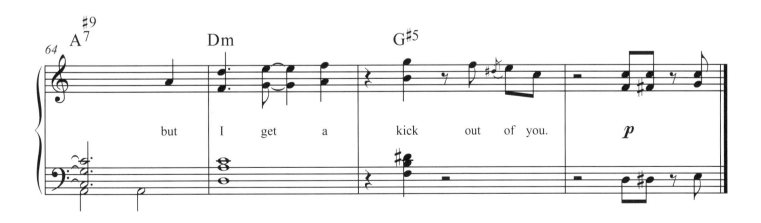

One for my Baby

Musik: Harold Arlen
Text: John Mercer
Arrangement: Carsten Gerlitz

66

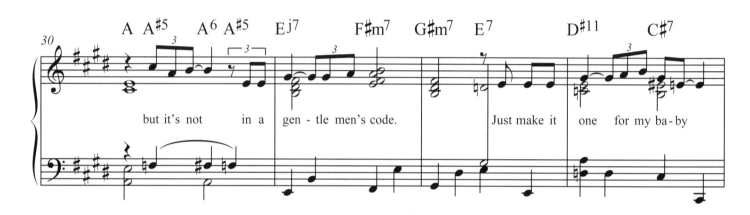

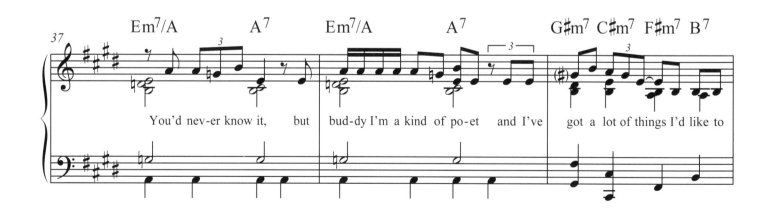

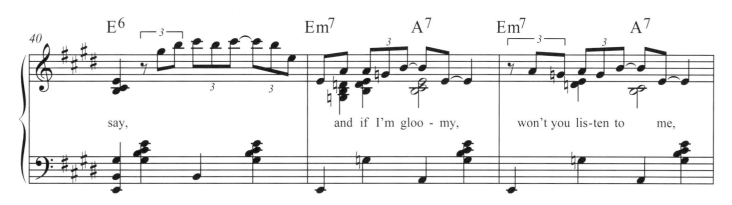

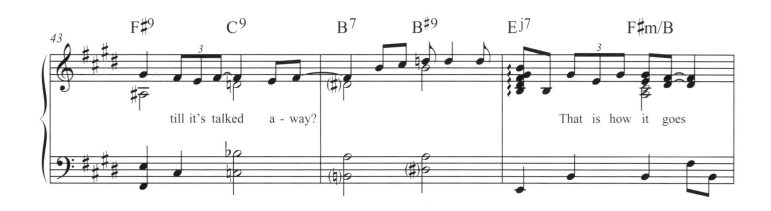

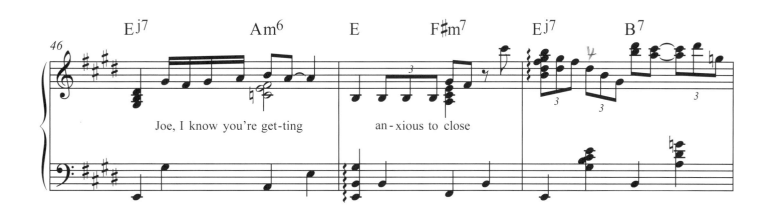

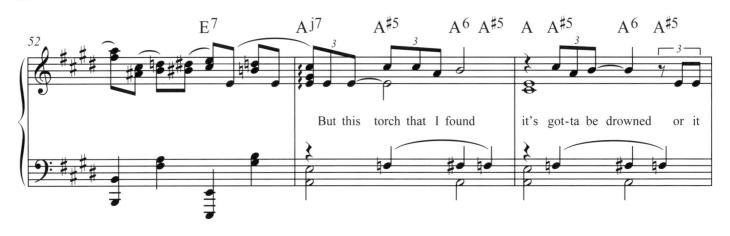

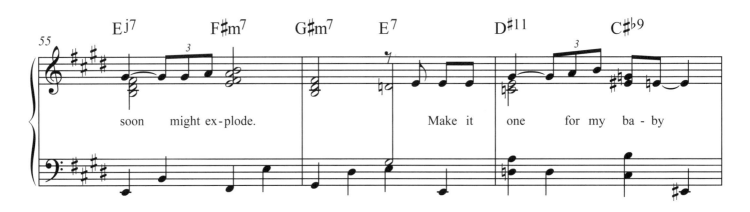

Body and Soul

Musik: John Green
Text: Edward Heyman, Robert Sour
Arrangement: Carsten Gerlitz

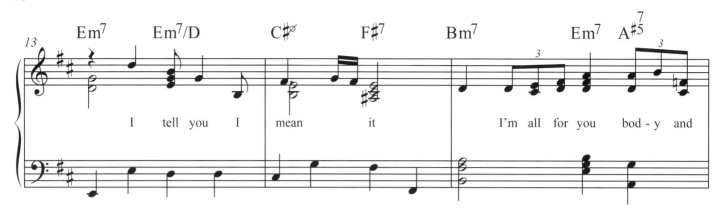

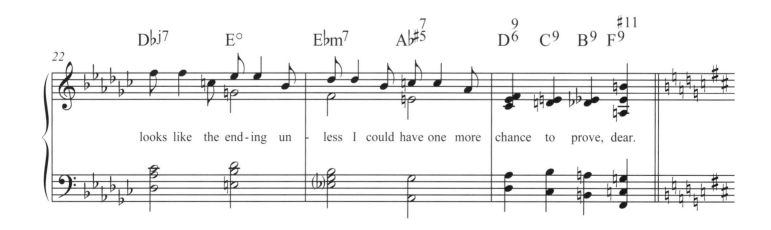

Schott Music, Mainz 52354